7 DEADLY DATES

JEAN-PAUL NOEL-CEPHISE

7 DEADLY DATES

First Published by Compass-Publishing 2017
www.compass-publishing.com

ISBN 978-1-912009-93-0
Printed by CPI Group UK Ltd (Croydon, CR0 4YY)

Edited and Typeset by Wrate's Editing Services, London.
www.wrateseditingservices.co.uk

This book is dedicated to Jean-Marie,
Suzy, Jordan, Brandon and Joseph

Contents

Introduction. 7

DATE 1 - DEADLY SIN: GLUTTONY - Stacey. 17

DATE 2 - DEADLY SIN: LUST - Madeline 27

DATE 3 - DEADLY SIN: GREED - Zoe. 35

DATE 4 - DEADLY SIN: SLOTH - Anna. 43

DATE 5 - DEADLY SIN: WRATH - Sofia. 53

DATE 6 - DEADLY SIN: PRIDE - Naomi 63

DATE 7 - DEADLY SIN: ENVY - Phoebe 75

Afterword 83

About the Author 89

Acknowledgements. 91

Introduction

Over the past decade, internet dating has gained huge popularity. In our busy, consumerist world, single people have welcomed the concept that online shopping can be extended to looking for a partner.

Personally, I've been able to bookmark my chosen dating website on my laptop and phone. I've even used an app in my search for love. This isn't much different to how I shop for shoes on Amazon and eBay. Happy days!

The location and specifics of your search can be managed flexibly from the comfort of your own bed before you've even brushed your teeth. Additionally, there are myriad websites to choose from, all with varying approaches to helping you find the perfect match.

Tinder allows you a direct, fast screen swipe to scroll through potential matches (right if you like them and left if you don't), whereas Guardian Soulmates, eHarmony and Elite Singles works by analysing in-depth personality profiles. Match, FirstMet, Lovestruck and Zoosk work on the basis of matching you with singles with similar characteristics.

As the names suggest, Christian Connection and Christian Mingle match members with common religious and spiritual beliefs.

You can choose someone based on their height, colour, build, hair type, eye colour, career, age, location, star sign and family status…and the list goes on and on.

So, how did I come to enter into this world? Well, six years ago my divorce completely transformed my home and social life. We cited irreconcilable differences as the reason for our separation, but I think we just didn't like each other enough to bother trying to reconcile them.

My parents have been married for over 40 years and I've always been proud of their successful, enduring partnership. As their only child, I felt a bit embarrassed about my own marriage failure, especially as I have two boys with my ex: a teenager and an 12 year old. My mum and dad have always loved spending time with their family, especially their grandchildren, and I guess I would have liked them to be proud of me as a family man.

The only way I can describe being divorced after a long marriage is that it was akin to stepping off a noisy train, only to be deafened by the silence. The initial peace after the marathon journey was pretty uncomfortable. It took me some time to adjust to being single again and begin to appreciate the peace and quiet in my life.

After a year or so, I felt I had the time and room in my life to begin a new relationship and I decided to start dating. I had a romantic dream of meeting a woman, falling in love and finding my Happy Ever After…a bit like Shrek.

For the past decade, I've worked as a freelance business studies lecturer, and I absolutely love my job. It allows me to travel all over London and the UK. However, the nature of private freelance teaching means there hasn't been much opportunity to form a relationship with work colleagues, namely because I haven't got any! My students may all be adults, but it would be unprofessional of me to date them.

I've been out with a few friends of friends and with women I've met at clubs and parties, but none of these dates have led to a solid relationship. So, like everyone else who has tried to date via the internet, I decided to turn to technology to help me find 'The One'…that elusive soul mate, partner, lady of my life. You get the picture.

I joined Match.com, wrote my profile and posted it online together with some honest but flattering recent pictures. I described myself accurately as weighing about 13 stone and having a large, athletic build (developed in my late teens through years of playing badminton, lifting weights and boxing). My pictures showed off my creamy brown complexion – inherited from my gorgeous Mauritian ancestors – as well as my brown eyes and black hair.

It's not always easy to write about yourself from an independent point of view. I focused on the positive, describing myself as kind, intelligent, patient and dry-witted. My friends say I'm understanding and determined. They also say some bad stuff too, but I decided not to put those things in my profile.

I wrote about what I enjoy doing and the list was no doubt similar to all other online dating profiles: eating out, playing sports, watching films, reading, spending time with friends, travelling to exotic countries and cooking tasty food. It seems that all over the planet we are doing the same sort of stuff.

I reread and edited my profile until I was satisfied I had presented the best version of me.

I also wrote explicitly about what I desired in a woman. I wanted to find a partner with whom I shared similar qualities. She should be kind, patient and fun. Enjoy going out sociably but also be happy chilling at home. It would be great if she had a decent job and good relationships with her family. I didn't mind what race or religion she was.

And, of course, she should be attractive. I like girls who are slim or athletic and who look after themselves, perhaps by exercising and having a good work-life balance. As I'm 5ft11, I wanted someone who was at least 5ft5.

I posted my profile and paid the three-month membership fee. Then, like a fisherman with his line in the lake, I periodically checked in to see who was nibbling at my profile.

Well, it wasn't very long before I began to gain attention from around the country. When women wanted to display their interest they would send me a wink, which I guess is a bit like saying, "What's up?" I couldn't believe that I was receiving so much attention and interest from lovely ladies across the UK. It made me feel great!

Apparently, one in five people are finding their partners online. This is great news if, like me, you don't have time to go trawling bars and clubs with the aim of finding love. Online dating is convenient and allows you access to a much wider pool of potential partners. It's like a global database of potentials, which you can work your way through and quickly decide who may be right for you.

Some people may still be a little sceptical about using the internet to find romance, but I wasn't afraid to give it a try. The process went as follows: scan the picture and then their profile. If interested, message the person, chat online for a bit and then arrange to meet up. It's actually all in reverse to how we date 'normally' in our lives. When you meet someone in a bar or at an event, you may chat for a while before discovering each other's basic personal details.

So it's much easier to get to know someone when you've met in person. But when meeting people via the internet, it helps to understand this reversed process a bit better.

What I discovered is that no matter how the person looked in their pictures, no matter how they described themselves in their profiles or how they sounded in their messages, there was *always* an element of surprise on the first date (FD). My dates were rarely put together exactly as I had thought they were.

7 Deadly Dates recounts the surprises I encountered and how I attempted to cope with them, while also trying to enjoy the date. After all, dating should be a fun experience, right? It should be enjoyable to go out and meet new people. The problem was that I had invested in the price of a subscription and my dream was to find my perfect partner, so how could it really be fun when the outcome was so important?

You might say there was a conflict of interest.

My experiences made me wonder about the remaining four out of five people. What happens to them? Do they find love elsewhere or are they permanently on the look out? And what happens to us hopeful folk as we work our way through more and more online dates, only to find we are not realising our dream of love and happiness? What happens to our fantasy of a Happy Ever After?

I had so many other questions too. Is it actually right to harness technology to find love? Are people truthful about themselves? Is there a right way to date online? A protocol? What can you post about yourself online that might make you seem attractive to someone reading about you? What if you're not great looking or you don't have a model physique?

Dating sites give you advice on how to present aspects of yourself, but do these apply to everyone? Some aspects of modern life make dating tough. The age of social media means there is an intense pressure on people to always look good, be entertaining and continuously attract positive attention.

What follows is my account of my internet dating journey, which took me far and wide and allowed me to meet a number of women who looked and sounded perfect for me. This is simply a view of dating from the perspective of a guy using the web to look for love and a steady relationship. It shouldn't have proved difficult. After all, I'm a presentable guy with an easy going personality (or so my friends tell me).

Each of the following 7 dates show that meeting people via the internet demands patience and skill. There is a *right* way to do it, because it's a completely *different* way to get to know someone. Dating via the internet adds a new dynamic to the whole courtship process. There's a layer of *pre-courtship* before the *actual courtship* can begin.

More often than not, the ladies I met were nice and a credit to their sex, but alas they were not a good match for me. Of course, I accepted that I'd need to kiss a few frogs before I found true love, but the fact was, for very surprising reasons that I'm about to let you in on, my dates didn't even come close to being perfect for me. One by one, they committed a Deadly Dating Sin.

Read on to discover what happened on my *7 Deadly*

Dates. They were sometimes comical, sometimes scary, sometimes shocking and sometimes sad, but always entertaining. At the end of this book you will have gained some insight into how much of a personal journey internet dating is, regardless of everyone else's experiences. For those of us who are seeking love, going online is as good a place as any to start. But it's best to appreciate early on that the path of internet dating is a unique one.

I've written this book for those hoping to find a partner through the web. In openly showing what happened to me on my dates and how I tried to learn positively from them, I hope that you will be able to appreciate how challenging it can really be for everyone, and not just for you.

Don't give up hope. Remember that there are many success stories from online dating. There are couples that just happened to hit upon the right approach and found their Happy Ever After.

Keep refining your approach, keep hopeful, get better at dating and you can find yours.

Jean-Paul

Please note, the names and certain details of my 7 Deadly Dates have been changed to protect their identities.

7

DEADLY

DATES

DEADLY SIN: GLUTTONY

Stacey

As I parked my car outside Bromley South train station for my first date with Stacey, I thought about our preliminary phone conversations and messages. Stacey worked as an HR Manager for a construction company. She had a degree in HR Management, so I knew she was academically bright. Outside work she volunteered as a youth leader in her local church. To unwind she liked going out with her friends for cocktails and exotic dinners.

Stacey was in her early 30s, 5ft6 and extremely pretty. She had long, black curly hair, blue eyes and Mediterranean, olive-coloured skin. Although she was slim, she still had nice curves and a great posture. She also had a lovely smile and light pink, full lips, all of which I found extremely appealing.

I met Stacey through Christian Mingle, a highly rated and inexpensive dating website that attracted members looking for matches with common spiritual beliefs.

After a few online messages, we exchanged numbers and spoke on the phone about three or four times before agreeing to meet. Stacey liked making wisecracks, so I knew she had a decent sense of humour, and we had a few good laughs on the phone. She was very cheeky and confident, which I found attractive.

Stacey had a sensitive side too. She told me about her past relationship with a guy she had done everything for, only to find he didn't want a future with her. He had then proceeded to date another girl from the same church. After being so publically humiliated, Stacey had to face both of them every Sunday.

I ruminated on my own divorce and saw that we shared some common ground. This ground, together with our conversations and Stacey's lovely pictures, left me with a sense that she could be 'The One'.

The One is an important role, just like Neo's role in *The Matrix*. (Now, for those of you who aren't familiar with the film, Neo was supposed to be the prophesised saviour of the slaves in Zion.) I was feeling pretty hopeful about what might develop between Stacey and me and hotly anticipated how it would reveal itself after we met.

Ahead of our first date, Stacey told me that as this was a special occasion, she was buying a new dress so she would look her best. I liked that, as it showed she was keen to make a good impression on me. So I made sure that I looked my best too. I put on a crisp, fresh white shirt, some black, smart trousers and my favourite light tan Italian shoes. A black blazer finished off my debonair look.

I hoped my choice of clothes would complement Stacey's dress. We would look like a couple out of *Strictly Come Dancing*. Maybe we would dazzle the crowds at the Thai restaurant I had booked in Crystal Palace.

As I waited outside Bromley station, I decided to up my game. I stepped out of my car, leaving my stereo pumping out Michael Jackson's *Thriller* album. I wanted to show Stacey how cool I was. As it was a warm evening, I took off my jacket and threw it over my shoulder, Michael Jackson-style. I popped my collar slightly and leant back against my car, pushing my Police shades further up my nose. Stacey was due to arrive at any minute.

A train station is usually quite an easy place to spot the person you're meeting for a first date. Commuters usually flood out of the station with purpose, keen to get onto the next leg of their journey. By contrast, people arriving for a date usually stop outside with an element of uncertainty. They look about them nervously, as though they're about to be stood up. My aim as the gentleman was to minimise Stacey's period of uncertainty.

Just then, a woman came out of the station looking about her as though she was lost. She was wearing a lovely sequined blue dress and silver shoes, and she was carrying a small silver handbag to match. She had shoulder length dark hair and light skin. She was dressed really well, but I knew it wasn't Stacey because she was very large – about a size 16. I wondered if she needed help to find her way.

She spotted me near my car and came across, presumably to ask for directions.

"Hi, are you Jean-Paul?"

I instantly recognised her lovely voice from our chats on the phone.

"This *can't* be Stacey," I thought.

If I was going to quantify it, I'd say this lady was about four stone heavier than the Stacey from the website. She was nowhere near slim and physically looked nothing like her photographs.

"I'm Stacey," she said, smiling nervously as she saw my hesitation.

It was indeed Stacey. 'The One.'

Putting it all together, I'd have to say I felt cheated, disappointed and frustrated all in one go. It was as though I had just been robbed. Robbed of my dreams. But I was also still in a kind of shock. Post-traumatic shock. I had really been looking forward to seeing the woman *in the pictures.*

It might sound fickle, but I wanted to go out with a woman who was *that* shape. Slim.

I managed to smile and say hi, but at this point I wanted to just get in my car and leave. Alone. The problem was that Stacey and I had spoken enough for a friendship to develop. And she had travelled a long way to come to meet me. And she'd been treated badly by her ex. And she had bought a new dress. And on top of all that we were supposed to be in *Strictly* tonight.

So I switched into gentleman mode. I kissed her politely on the cheek and invited her to get into the car.

Stacey was happy to be there. She was chatty and friendly and talked about her journey on the train and other things that I couldn't quite absorb. My mind was blank. "I need a large drink," I thought, "and food". This is most guys' solution to any predicament. Alcohol and food.

We headed to the Thai restaurant and parked up before walking in together.

"I can do this," I thought calmly. "We'll have a drink together and some food, then I'll drive her back to the station and go home."

I had an urge to talk to Stacey about the pictures I'd seen and trusted online. I wanted to shout, "Whose pictures did you post online, coz they're definitely not yours?" I wanted to tell her that I was really shocked and disappointed and that I was leaving immediately. I wanted to tell her exactly how let down I felt. But I didn't. I was too polite and couldn't think of a way to tell her how I felt without referring to her size and offending her. So I shut my mouth and stayed silent. I must have had a pained look on my face.

As we walked into the restaurant, I assumed an air of friendship. I did this by trying not to show Stacey any special attention, ensuring I walked in front of her instead of remaining at her side. I behaved as if we were mates out for dinner. The problem was, Stacey wasn't reading from the same script.

Right from the off, she was exceptionally frisky. Her bright blue eyes constantly checked me out and her body language was quite openly flirtatious. Before we were seated, she was never more than two inches away from me. After we'd taken our place at the table, the first thing Stacey asked for was a large glass of white wine. I joined her in a Sauvignon Blanc. I needed to take a hit and calm down from the initial shock.

I had composed myself enough now to take the view that this was going to be a short dinner, with me being a gentleman. I decided I could play that role pretty well.

The waiter grinned at me as he took our order. I wasn't sure what was tickling him, but I didn't share his amusement. I ordered a Pad Thai (my favourite noodle dish) and a Thai green curry. Stacey ordered some tamarind duck, a portion of sticky rice and some steamed dumplings. As the waiter took off with our order, we engaged in some frivolous chitchat, with me secretly keeping an eye on the time via the clock behind Stacey's seat.

Her drink finished inside five minutes, Stacey ordered another one directly through the waiter.

"You don't mind?" she asked me as an afterthought.

"Of course not," I said, smiling politely. I was, after all, a gentleman.

Stacey did most of the talking. She chatted away about her family, friends, job and ambitions. All I kept asking myself was what had possessed her to post such a huge lie on the website.

After the same smirking waiter had delivered Stacey's second glass of wine, she polished it off inside the same record time and quickly ordered another large one. For this one she finally slowed down the pace of her swallowing, but it was already too late. Stacey had started to get *loud*.

The restaurant was already getting busy so I guess you'd have to speak up a little to be heard, but Stacey's pleasant phone voice had raised a couple of decibels and had also gone up an octave. She was already slightly drunk by the time our food arrived. I estimated the eating time to be 25 minutes and added on a minimum of ten minutes chatting time before we could leave.

But, of course, Stacey had her own agenda and it involved eating as slowly as possible, swallowing yet more wine and giggling loudly. At one point she tried to play footsie with me under the table before realising she was actually rubbing her foot along the table leg. At that moment she called out loudly, "Ooh, there seems to be something in between my legs under the table!"

All I could do was smile politely and eat more quickly. When we'd finished our meals, Stacey asked if she could have a Baileys to wash down her meal with. I said I thought she'd had enough. It was clear that her constant seeking of permission for drinks meant she had no intention of even offering to pay towards the meal.

Both my dreams and my wallet were experiencing the grief of loss.

I pretended to yawn and said I was going to call it a night, as I had to work the next day. At this point Stacey's whole demeanour changed.

"You don't want to see me again, do you?" she asked with a heavy voice and sorrowful look. "You don't like me, do you?"

"Don't be silly!" I said smiling. "You're lovely. Really you are." I was trying hard not to make eye contact.

I asked for the bill and paid it while trying to look happy rather than like I'd just been robbed, before finally ushering Stacey into the car and driving back towards Bromley.

"You know, I don't have to go home yet. It's still early," Stacey said. "Do you live far from here?"

"Not far really," I said trying to keep my voice as pleasant as possible. "But I'm so tired. And I have to work tomorrow." I pretended to yawn and kept my eyes on the road.

My aim was to get Stacey directly to the station. Monopoly came to mind. "Do not pass Go. Do not collect $200," I told myself. "Go straight to Bromley station."

I parked outside the station, turned to Stacey and said, "Thanks for a lovely evening."

"Do you want to see me again?" she asked with a sad but expectant look in her eyes.

On a first date, if you mutually agree to meet again in the flow of conversation then that's cool. But what if someone asks you at the end of the date if you want to see them again and you don't want to? Do you tell them to their face? Lie? Say you don't know?

Anything other than saying yes to meeting again will just bring more questions and possibly a backlash of emotions, extending the time it takes to exit your date. So my advice is that if you get to the end of the night and the subject hasn't come up, do not discuss it when you want to leave and go home. It could cost you more time and force you to have to justify your reasons. Just be polite and say you'll get back to them.

"I've no objections to seeing you again," I said. (In my head, I was screaming, "I *do* object to your blatant lies on the website!") I didn't add that I meant seeing her again as friends or as colleagues, while at a supermarket or a party, or anything else that I believed would be appropriate for Stacey. I just let her assume what I meant.

Stacey waited a minute for a kiss, I assume, then, once she realised that none was coming, kissed my cheek and said goodnight before getting out of the car. I watched her walk into the station, waited for a few minutes out of courtesy, then sadly drove home.

The last thoughts I had before I fell asleep in my comfortable bed were how awful fraud can be. It's not only committed in companies through money laundering, but also through internet dating, where people describe themselves inaccurately and post pictures of themselves from a previous decade.

This is so unfair for people like me who are looking for honesty within a relationship. The point was that Stacey had lied about herself by posting pictures, which had about a quarter of her missing. If I'd been a lawyer, I'd have said she had a duty of care to disclose this information. As an accountant I'd have said she had a duty to disclose all her assets.

Worse than that, we had spoken on the phone and she never mentioned her pictures. It was just like committing fraud.

Your pictures should be recent and your description should be 'Sale of Goods' accurate. Lying about appearances is a no no. No sale would ever take place if the goods didn't match their descriptions. The pre-courtship had been a waste of time and so was the actual date. It was totally unethical behaviour by Stacey.

I decided to ask all my future dates to confirm that their pictures were recent. This might be an awkward request and it may make me appear a little fickle about looks, but who cares? It's so important.

Maybe I could ask for their picture via email, WhatsApp, Facebook, Instagram or Snapchat. This would be the beginning of a checklist, which I planned to develop further. The idea was for me to run through the checklist casually on the phone with my potential date *before* agreeing to meet up.

Stacey rang me in the week and apologised for her behaviour at the restaurant, citing nerves as her reason for getting gluttonously drunk and loud on our first date. I could understand that. I could have also forgotten it and met her again as a friend, if the person I met was the person she had posted online.

We never spoke about her fraudulent description.

DEADLY SIN: LUST

Madeline

Guardian Soulmates is a reputable dating site. It has *The Guardian* newspaper brand behind it and boasts great reviews from users. It's a bit more expensive than the likes of Match and eHarmony, but I figured the higher the investment in a reputable dating site, the better the return was likely to be. Being a trained accountant, I go in for that whole risk vs reward concept. It's sad really.

Within a few days of signing up, I had the interest of two ladies. The second one, Madeline, was physically very appealing. She was 5ft7, had light skin, dark green eyes and straight, shoulder-length blonde hair. She also had a slim, hourglass figure and looked as if she might play professional tennis. In short, she was a babe.

Madeline also had an executive job working as a Procurement Director. Domestically she was a mum to a 10-year-old daughter, and this also appealed to me. She was experienced at parenthood, which would be beneficial down the line should she become part of my family.

Madeline was very open in terms of what she wanted from a relationship. I found this openness refreshing, if a bit surprising. She told me she wanted to fall in love with a wonderful man who could be her partner and a father to her daughter. She wanted them all to bond and eventually live the dream of a perfect family life together.

When you're choosing a partner, it's important to consider that if you're living with your own kids then their feelings and opinions can make or break a relationship. My eldest son lives with me and my younger one spends roughly half his time at mine, and the rest with his mum. So their opinions and feelings will naturally influence my relationship with a woman, especially if we get to the point of sharing a home.

But it's more than that. You actually want everyone to be able to get along and live in bliss. Your kids are your closest family, or at least they should be. And they've been through enough crap from a broken relationship without you experimenting on them in the future with any old person you're taking a chance on. The question is: "When is it the right time to introduce a person to your kids?"

I think it would be quite natural to invite someone into your life and home, as long as you've got a basic friendship, although maybe not after just one date!

Madeline said that she was an amazing cook and enjoyed making Sunday roasts, as well as a variety of different dishes in the week. She went to the gym a lot to try to keep in shape. I couldn't comment on the cooking front, but it looked to me that she had succeeded in the shape category. She was into a wide range of music and appeared to be an energetic woman. She mentioned a few times how she was looking forward to spending long weekends with her new partner.

We chatted online for a few days. All her messages were well written and polite. She was bright and seemed emotionally intelligent. She was quite open about her feelings for the people she liked, such as her friends and family. She loved her daughter to bits and really craved another long-term relationship.

To me, it's a good sign if someone has been in a long-term relationship, as it demonstrates the commitment they're able to give to another person. On the other hand, it could also mean that they're unable to leave poor relationships due to low self-esteem.

How do you tell the difference? Good question. Just ask them to describe their ex-partner!

By the time that we met, we had spoken twice on the phone and had a good rapport. Madeline was quite intuitive and asked plenty of questions about my boys and me. She took a real interest in their ages and what they did for fun. She genuinely seemed like a caring woman. She had a lot to offer and I was honoured that I could be the one to potentially collect it all.

For our first date we met at Victoria station. I arrived before her and sat in Frankie & Benny's facing the door so that I could see her arrival. It was a bit like being in a castle on a high hill and witnessing your enemy approach from afar. Only this was not the enemy. I had a good feeling about Madeline.

After a few minutes I spotted her walking towards me. From about 10-feet away she looked quite gorgeous. She had come from work and was smartly dressed in white, skin-tight jeans and a light green shirt. She was a fine figure of a woman and walked confidently towards my table. As she did so, I could see some passers-by giving her a second glance.

At point-blank range, I could tell that Madeline looked at least 10 years older than she did in her pictures. She looked around 48. I liked the idea of dating an older, more experienced woman, but I knew instantly this was the look of a woman who had been through a difficult life. Her body was in excellent shape, but I was disappointed that facially she didn't look like she did in her pictures. She looked very tired. I switched on sympathetic mode and waited.

Madeline was relaxed, polite and watched me attentively while we shared a few snacks and got through a bottle of Malbec. At some point she told me how lovely I was and I spotted tears in her eyes as she thanked me for the date. She said how grateful she was for the opportunity to meet a decent guy.

She then proceeded to tell me how in her younger days she was a podium dancer at various nightclubs. I've watched these women at clubs in central London and they dance in cages rather than around poles. It's less skilful, but the cage has bondage undertones and this can be very erotic under the laser lights.

Under the Malbec truth serum, Madeline revealed that as well as being a podium dancer, she had been a heavy weed smoker, had done a fair amount of coke (not the cola variety) and had enjoyed a very expressive sexual life before transforming into the dedicated mum she now was. She now wanted the perfect family with a new partner. And here she was fixating on me.

The trouble was, her background was a bit too much for me to process on a first date. I found myself feeling a bit disappointed with the whole thing. You can't exactly ask people to provide their full service history on the phone, can you? As I mulled over this, Madeline carried on drinking the wine. I think she was celebrating her new relationship. I drank more to try and hide my disappointment. I ordered a second bottle and Madeline and I began to get drunk together.

She was interesting company and when she began to flirt I didn't try to stop her. She leant across to kiss me and her lips were soft and sweet. As people so often do, my date used her body language to communicate that she was feeling a strong sense of lust towards me. Her pheromones were bombarding me with ripe overtones and I found myself beginning to feel physically attracted to her.

Of course, the second bottle of Malbec was having a devastating effect on my higher consciousness. Isn't this so often the case? How many close physical encounters in our lives have been initiated with a few alcoholic drinks inside us, which have reduced our inhibitions to nil and put our confidence into turbo?

Suddenly, Madeline and I were like lusty teenagers: we were giggling, kissing and cuddling each other in public. We held hands as though we had been together for weeks. "This is crazy," I thought. It was a euphoria induced by alcohol. After a while the wine began to loosen its effect on me and I started to lose my enthusiasm for the roller coaster ride.

The question was: how was I going to regain my composure after we had been acting like teenagers in love? Madeline was a pleasant person and I really didn't want to hurt her feelings. Alright, so her pictures were out of date and she had a past life, but who doesn't? We have all had some historic issues to deal with in our lives. The trouble was, I didn't really want to learn about them *all* on a first date.

As with before, I realised I should have asked Madeline for a recent picture to verify exactly how she looked. I should have let her know before we met that I was expecting her to look just like her photographs. If a person has put on 20 pounds or noticeably aged since their last snaps – or maybe even got shorter – you need to know. Ask them!

Madeline didn't look exactly like her pictures, yet she was still attractive. As a person she just wasn't appealing to me as a suitable partner. She expected to see me again, but I knew I didn't want that to happen. It's nice to learn about someone over a series of dates, but I'd already heard her entire life story. There didn't seem to be a point to meeting again, as I knew everything I needed to know. I had to be fair to her and me.

"It's getting late," I said, trying to sound like I was surprised the evening had already come to an end. "We probably should call it a night. I don't want you going home too late."

Madeline agreed and then asked me when I was next free to meet up. She suggested we could meet closer to her North London home.

Again, it seemed inappropriate at this point for me to talk about whether I wanted to meet up for a second time. I know this wasn't very honest or open of me, but Madeline was already emotional and tearful while we were having fun. What on earth would she be like if I told her I didn't want to see her again?

I think that we should be as honest as possible in life, but the problem with honesty is that it needs constant justification – and that can be exhausting. Also, for some reason, when women take a liking to me there is an expectation that I should be a gentleman and accommodate their feelings. The same expectation doesn't seem to apply in reverse.

Men are less likely to initiate the decision to go out with a woman. We are generally considered to be the hunters and we ask their permission to go out with them. This is why guys often bail out on asking girls out. We are scared to be let down, with no soothing explanation for our egos.

Madeline and I kissed and said our goodbyes like a young couple separating after a holiday romance.

I waited until she was a safe distance away and then sent her a long message via WhatsApp to explain my thoughts and feelings as briefly as possible. I explained that even though we'd had a lovely date, I didn't feel we would be right for each other. I read and reread my message before hitting send. I wanted to ensure it was as polite and considerate as possible. Still, I was sure that it wouldn't be well received. And I was right. Madeline had a mini explosion (via WhatsApp), to the effect that she was a victim of love deprivation in life and had lost faith in all mankind forever. I found myself feeling thankful I had managed to avoid this meltdown in person.

Maybe if I'd asked her for more details about her past experiences on the phone, it would have helped me get a clearer picture of who she was. People are always changing, so a person's history is not always who they are today, but it is an indication. If I'd done this, maybe we could have avoided meeting in the first place.

I decided not to get drunk on a first date ever again.

DEADLY SIN: GREED

Zoe

Zoe, the next woman I met through *Guardian Soulmates,* was fairly attractive, but it was her profile that tickled me. It was comical and she made me laugh. Zoe made some funny quips about the things she liked to do in her spare time, such as knitting, which showed she didn't take herself too seriously.

Zoe was in her mid-thirties and had one child from a previous relationship. She was about 5ft4, with a pear-shaped figure, and she was into badminton, which I also enjoy playing. Running around the court is actually harder than it looks. Zoe also had a black belt in karate. She was quite a diverse person and seemed to be stress free. "Let's find out more," I thought.

If nothing else, with her karate skills, Zoe would be able to take care of me when we went out in public and could act as my personal bodyguard. Kind of like Mr Han and his harem in Bruce Lee's *Enter the Dragon.* (For those of you who aren't familiar with the film, the harem was made up of female martial arts experts, who were all very dangerous.)

After I had attracted Zoe's attention, we exchanged

a few messages. We then swapped numbers and spoke twice for about an hour before agreeing to meet for a coffee. While we chatted, I managed to analyse the main points on my checklist and Zoe seemed a good match.

For our first date, we met in Southampton. Zoe lived in Hampshire, which is where my parents still live today. I like this county. The countryside is visually stimulating and people are generally more relaxed than they are in London and Croydon.

I grew up in the town of Andover, Hampshire, and came to London when I was about 18. Like most country kids who come to London, I like the city life and enjoy the variety it offers. Maybe Zoe would help me get back to my country roots and learn to relax more. I had a pleasant vision of us in country pubs and taking long walks close to the river – perhaps with a dog.

I was running a little late for the date and when I messaged Zoe to let her know she told me she was already in Starbucks, where we'd agreed to meet.

"What shall I order for you?" she messaged back.

I was impressed with her kindness and thoughtfulness. Some women won't ask you this on a first date, as they believe the man should do the ordering. Zoe was generous and friendly. She went up a notch in my book.

When I arrived at the café, I had a hot chocolate waiting for me. The one with a dollop of fresh cream bobbing on top of it like an iceberg. Chocolate flakes were spread out around it, resembling chlorella on a pond, and there was a marshmallow on the side.

"Yum," I thought. I felt spoiled already. A date is a place where we give and receive positive attention. Although some people date *purely* to get attention, and maybe that can become a bit addictive after a while.

Zoe was prettier in person than in her pictures. She had red hair, lovely piercing blue eyes, full pink lips and dimples in her cheeks when she smiled. She was cute. She was a bit nervous, which I also found cute. It made me think that she cared about the outcome of our first date. If someone isn't a *little* nervous then it could mean they're not that bothered about meeting you in the first place.

My date was dressed in jeans and a jumper and a thick winter coat. The setting was nice and relaxed and I was in the mood for romance.

The trouble was, Zoe was a little too intense. She wasn't just a bit intense, she was very intense, and wouldn't even break eye contact with me. I was worried that if she didn't blink her eyes would dry out. Or worse, pop out. She didn't smile too much either, and that made me feel a bit edgy.

Zoe's eyebrows wouldn't come down, so she looked almost permanently surprised to see me. I felt like joking with her that she shouldn't look so shocked, as I'd been there for half an hour already, but of course I didn't. It was a shame, but my date wasn't exactly witty in person. It seemed that Zoe and her profile were divorced on the grounds of humour.

She fired off lots of questions and I could see her nodding and mentally noting my answers. I felt that I was in an interview and the outcome was very important. I guess Zoe was doing in person what I'd already done in our phone chats. I wondered if I would pass or fail.

A few of the questions she asked were the same ones she'd posed on the phone. I considered whether she was comparing my answers and trying to catch me out. To try and change the subject and get her to relax, I complimented her on her profile.

"It really made me smile," I said.

Zoe liked the praise. She stopped the interview and we talked about our previous dates. She had been internet dating for a few months and prior to that had been in several relationships over the course of two years. Her boyfriends ranged in age between 30 and 40 and she'd gone out with them for between two and eight months.

Within an hour I began to feel tired from chatting with Zoe. She was a nice woman, but she wouldn't relax at all. I got the impression this date was extremely important to her and I couldn't work out why. We had spoken twice before meeting up and she had seemed more relaxed on the phone than in person. As far as I could tell she was a nice person. She was fairly attractive, in good shape financially, had a lovely daughter and enjoyed good relationships with her friends and family.

She should have been more relaxed and comfortable with me than she was.

After an hour I asked her if she would like a cake, as it was getting close to lunchtime. My plan was to feed her something sweet to make her relax, and then take off on a wave of sugar-infused contentment back to my car and then my Croydon manor.

Zoe chose a slice of carrot cake, but before I had a chance to select my own treat, she said, "It's too much for me, can we share it?"

This wasn't a terrible suggestion. Sharing a slice of cake isn't like eating the same slice of pizza or dining on oysters together, is it? But although it's not exactly intimate, I didn't like the idea of sharing a piece of cake with a woman I'd just met. It was a little bit too much sharing at this point in our relationship. I wasn't ready for that.

"OK," I said. After all, I think it's a good idea to try and keep an open mind when sharing experiences with other people. Rather than say no to things you don't want to do or are scared of, it's better to say "yes" to things and enrich your life experience. Just like Jim Carey decides to do in the film, *The Yes Man*. If anything, I figured it might at least cure Zoe's nerves.

We had a fork each and I made sure I ate from the end of the cake nearest to me. The plan was that by the time we met in the middle I could stop eating just before I reached her side. That would protect me from getting contaminated with any bacteria.

By the way, I know full well this is something Sheldon might do in *The Big Bang Theory*. (For those of you who don't watch the American sitcom, Sheldon is a scientist who has terrible OCD and a fear of catching germs. This makes it impossible for him to share certain things with people or to get too close to anyone on any level. I totally get his point.)

After feeling like I'd been forced to partake in this ritual with Zoe, I was keen to wrap up our date more quickly. Having children has some handy alternative uses when you need to be somewhere else pronto. I told her that I had to go and pick up my kids from school. How was Zoe to know they had been using Oyster cards on London transport for years?

"I had a good time," I said politely. "Thank you."

"I'll walk you to your car," said Zoe, a bit too sweetly.

"No!" I thought to myself "I just want to leave now!"

I think it's a bad idea to let a woman walk you to your car at the end of an unsuccessful date. You'll be a sitting duck, forced to engage more before you can drive away. It's best to say goodbye and then go to your car alone. I guess that women must feel the same and take similar precautions.

"That's OK, Zoe," I said cheerfully. "I'm not even exactly sure where I parked."

This seemed like a good way to excuse myself and also to ensure that we couldn't walk together, as it seemed that I didn't even know which direction I was going in.

"Oh no!" Zoe said, being really helpful. "I'll have to help you find it. I don't want you wandering around looking for it when you have to drive back to your kids."

Zoe seemed determined to help. My short-term amnesia disappeared and I managed to locate my car very quickly. After kissing her on the cheek lightly, I got into my car and started the engine.

"I'll contact you later," I said as casually as I could. I didn't want to put too much emphasis on having to call. That's why texting was invented, right?

I have tinted windows in my car. Before I could drive off, Zoe tapped on the window and ushered me to wind down my window. I edged it down about a third of the way and looked at her enquiringly through the gap.

"Can I ask you something?" she smiled.

"Sure," I replied. I was really hoping it wasn't going to be about a second date because I wasn't sure how I was going to fend off that possibility.

"I don't want to wait 'til our second date for a kiss," Zoe smiled coyly. "Can I get one now?"

Now, for many guys, this might be a welcome luxury. It can be part of the spoils of dating if you're lucky. A bonus. But for me it represented no such thing. I didn't fancy Zoe. She had been draining to be with and I wasn't in the mood for kissing her. At all.

I quickly calculated the odds of her wanting a long kiss on the lips and worked out it was more likely she was only after a quick peck. As this was such an awkward moment and I wanted to get it over and done with as soon as possible, I only wound down the window until it was half way.

Zoe leaned her head through the window and extended her neck like a T-Rex at Jurassic Park getting to sniff her prey.

Then she planted her lips against mine. I'm sure the kiss lasted no longer than a few seconds, but time *stopped* for what seemed like an eternity. I heard the scream "CLEAR!" before the electric current ran through time and resuscitated it so that my kiss of death could end.

I managed to smile at Zoe and tried to look cool as she smirked at me with a look of satisfaction, as if to say, "Got you, sucker!"

The odds of a quick peck on the lips had not been in my favour. My lips are full and are an expressive feature of my face. But afterwards they seemed to shrink away inside my mouth for a while, as if they wanted avoid further contact with the outside world. They were traumatised.

I washed my mouth and lips with the emergency mouthwash I kept in the car and tried to convince myself that the date hadn't been so bad. I also realised what Zoe's objective had been all along. She messaged me later to apologise for being so greedy for a kiss. I laughed it off saying it could have happened to anyone.

Truthfully I wish it *had* happened to anyone. Anyone but me.

I wondered why she had been so tense. She must have been that way during our phone calls, but I only spoke with her twice, which wasn't enough for me to pick up on that. I thought that we had enough in common to make it worth a meet-up, so I didn't analyse the phone chats too much. I'd been too busy concentrating on my checklist.

Looking back, I think you need some time in between the phone chats to allow yourself to settle down with each other and relax. Otherwise, the hype of chatting to someone new and the chance of meeting them quickly takes over. This prospect is always exciting, but I think slowing it down just a bit can reveal more and save precious time in the future. If I'd spoken with Zoe a few more times before we met, I'd have realised she was very intense by nature.

She rang me the next day to ask me when I was free to meet up again. I politely explained that although she was a very nice girl, she lived too far away for me to consider a relationship with her.

DEADLY SIN: SLOTH

Anna

I met Anna, a lovely looking eastern European girl, through eHarmony. We were matched due to our career choices, as we both work in accounting. The finance industry is so filled with glamour that only the coolest people work in it. I imagined us as a sophisticated couple attending finance functions together.

Our profiles matched in several other categories too. We liked the same kind of music and food and had similar positive and humorous personality types. She played the piano professionally part-time and I was impressed that she also had a creative side.

My match had long blonde hair, with thin black streaks, and hazel eyes. At 5ft6 she was my ideal height and had a voluptuous figure. She liked going to the gym, had a good job and seemed to have an active social life. She'd written her profile in a laid back-style, as though she wasn't taking writing it too seriously.

So she was fit, artistic, funny, sophisticated and local to me. What more could a man possibly ask for?

I found myself attracted to the virtual Anna even before sending her an email. Sometimes I find communicating with someone on a dating website quite frustrating. I'd send a message and then receive a response the next day. Then I'd reply later in the week. Before I knew it, a week had gone by without a proper conversation having taken place. Lots of guys seem to like this form of communicating because it allows you to speak to many people at the same time. The problem is that you never really get to know any one person. You're basically just paying a membership to get attention and flirt. Our needs must be fulfilled I suppose, so maybe it's a good investment for some people.

But Anna and I exchanged messages online quite quickly then swapped mobile numbers so we could hear each other's voices. I was glad she had responded to my messages and hoped we would hit it off.

Anna was from Poland and I really liked her accent. She spoke very good English, but with a lilt that made her all the more irresistible. I like women with a nice accent, although it does depend on where the accent is from. Spanish and Italian ones are sexy, but I'm really not sure about British and German ones.

Our first conversation was fascinating. Anna was easy to talk to. So easy to talk to. She was very laid back and came across as intelligent but also witty and chilled. And she was a good listener. I don't make that statement lightly about any person I've dated. The art of listening is a true skill that many people don't possess. To many people, listening means waiting for their turn to speak.

Listening is *not* the same as hearing.

I can't see how any partnership can work when one person doesn't listen properly. I mean, how are you going to develop a relationship with anyone on the planet when you don't actually listen? What I've found in relationships is that a person's ability to listen is also directly affected by the level of emotion they are experiencing at the time of listening.

The calmer a person is, the better their ability to listen to what you're saying. Anna was a good listener and didn't seem to be highly emotional. I lived in hope.

We spoke about our family backgrounds, then our careers, then our favourite foods, then the drinks we liked, then our dreams for the future. All in, we spoke for about two hours on the phone. When I ended the call my ears were ringing from mobile radiation.

Indeed, love can cause earache as well as heartache.

Over the past decade, I've known a lot of guys who have had Polish girlfriends and they all seem to have had happy relationships with them. What I learned about Polish girls from our conversations is that they are traditional and value family and home life. They seem loyal and fairly calm, and they are often beautiful.

Before meeting up with Anna, I had to take a chill pill. I had to do this because, quite frankly, she had got me really interested. If her picture could be trusted then she was gorgeous. And she was intelligent, witty and financially stable. And she could cook! So I had to calm myself down a little. I was going to have to style this one out. After all, this could be Wifey.

We were due to meet later in the week in Crystal Palace and I wanted it to go really well. I got the feeling that Anna was more honest and straightforward than either Stacey or Madeline had been. My checklist had more ticks on it for this date than on any of the others. It looked like an exam script.

I've never gone shopping prior to a date before. I've got enough clothes to be able to make a decent selection for most occasions, and I usually go to a date dressed smart-casual. I like to make an effort to look clean and presentable. My hair is shaved and neat and my breath, of course, always smells minty fresh.

My underwear and shoes are always clean too. Women quite often notice a man's shoes because they usually have a few pairs to choose from themselves. Some women have many. I once asked a woman why she had so many shoes for only one pair of feet. Her answer was that shoes express more about a person than any other type of clothing.

If you really want to impress a woman with your clothes then wear decent shoes.

On this occasion, I decided to go out and buy a brand new shirt for the date. I wouldn't normally be so flamboyant on a FD, but frankly I was a bit wired about this one and wanted to look terrific. I chose a light blue, fitted Ben Sherman shirt from House of Fraser, which cost about £100. As I looked at myself in the mirror, Ed Sheeran was singing *Shape of You* in the background. Clearly this was a sign that Anna was going to like meeting me *and* my shirt on our date.

We met in a cocktail bar and Anna was as gorgeous as in her picture, if not more so. Her hair was ravishingly long. In order to get to explore that thick, blonde, flowing mane it would need a date all of its own.

Anna was dressed in a knee-length black dress with sparkles on the shoulders and black, sparkly open-toe heels. A long, silver-grey coat was perched on her shoulders. Her hazel eyes seemed to soften a bit when she saw me. She was looking at me intently, taking me all in.

Women dress very cleverly. Anything that sparkles will attract attention. Of course, that's what we all desire. The attention.

Anna was marvellous company. She was relaxed and carefree and had opinions on a wide variety of subjects. I bought us a round of drinks and she had no problem in generously buying the next one. There was a good, positive vibe opening up between us, accompanied, of course, by a few drinks.

We talked about her life back in Poland and we both agreed that even though England was the best country to live in, Spain seemed like a good place to emigrate to one day. We both liked warmer weather and more exotic surroundings than the UK has to offer.

I was dressed in a dark pair of tight jeans and, of course, The Shirt. Periodically, I patted the tops of my shoulders or ran my hands down the side of my arms casually, in order to bring Anna's attention to Ben. He had cost me a packet and I wanted him to fully express himself to Anna.

"That's a really nice shirt," she commented, looking at my chest.

"This?" I asked casually, raising and looking at my arms one by one. "Oh, I bought this recently. I've been waiting for a special occasion to wear it."

Anna seemed to appreciate both the shirt and the mention of our date as a special occasion.

We spent the rest of the evening at a pub two doors away. They had a live jazz band, and we managed to squeeze in a couple of dances. Anna wasn't a great mover, but she was fun and sexy and that was enough for me.

We danced to everything that night from Beyoncé and Sean Paul's *Baby Boy*, to Wham's cheesy 80s number, *I'm Your Man*. More than once Anna complimented me on my dance moves. Generally there is an assumption that if you're a good dancer then you can also move well in more intimate situations. I'm not sure whether the link between dance floor moves and mattress manoeuvres is true but I'm willing to stand on that platform of myth.

Finally, at about 11pm, Anna and I decided to leave the pub. There was a strange smell coming from there by that time. I assumed someone had probably just walked in off the streets after stepping in something unpleasant, or they had forgotten to put on their deodorant.

Anna lived in Crystal Palace and asked me if I would walk her home. We were getting on very well and there was a good chemistry between us, so I was only too happy to walk her to her house. If anything, at least I would know where she lived so I could offer to pick her up the next time we met. Yes, for the first time on my online dating journey I was hoping for a second date.

If a woman is happy for you to walk her home after a date then that is a very good indication she trusts you. It was a very short walk. Anna lived on the second floor of a huge, three-story house. I walked her to her door and leant forward to give her a kiss before saying goodnight.

We kissed slowly on the lips. Anna's lips were soft, full and slightly moist from her deep pink lip-gloss. She was a passionate kisser. I could feel a tingling in my feet. This was far from the Jurassic experience with Zoe. Then she asked me, "Would you like to come upstairs for a drink?"

There has been lots of advice written about this moment at the end of a date. The only thing I can say is that in life you should do what feels right and makes you happy. As long as it doesn't directly hurt someone else, of course.

"Yes," I replied. A current of excitement ran through my stomach, although I wasn't really sure what to expect. I didn't know Anna well enough for anything more than a drink, but we'd had a great evening, and here I was walking up the stairs behind a beautiful woman, about to enter her home. My male ego was inflating with every step.

Anna opened her door and we went inside. She lived in a cramped room with a double bed and a sink in the corner. There was access to a tiny balcony through the window and a curtain to the right of the room, behind which a little alcove had been turned into a walk-in wardrobe.

I had nowhere to sit but on the bed and I felt like I had invaded Anna's personal space. The room felt really compact. Because of the amount of booze I'd had at the pub I was going to need to use the toilet pretty soon.

"Damn!" I thought. "I hope the toilet's not in this room as well!"

Anna said she was going to change into something more comfortable and promptly disappeared behind the curtain concealing the wardrobe. I couldn't hear her anymore. She was gone for quite a while and I began to wonder if she'd gone to visit Narnia through the wardrobe.

I sat on the bed uncomfortably and then suddenly realised I could still detect the unpleasant smell from the pub.

"Oh my gosh!" I thought to myself. "I've only gone and

stepped in the same crap someone walked into the pub a while back."

I checked my shoes and was relieved to find nothing on the soles except worn out leather. Anxiously, I checked my clothing for anything that might be giving off this horrid odour. Then I looked around.

"Where is that smell coming from?" I thought. "How the hell has it followed us here?"

Finally, Anna came back into her tiny den. With her arrival, the smell intensified. Horrified, I realised that the stench I'd thought had come from some stranger in the pub had all the while been emanating from my beautiful date. As the evening had worn on, maybe her deodorant had worn off too.

Body odour is not something you can pick up on in a picture or a general profile. It must be experienced in person. And it can be disguised by perfumes and deodorants. I couldn't imagine leaving my house for a first date without using these products. I've never seen a category for a body odour description on a dating site. Perhaps there should be one, as it's so important to some of us. Maybe the site could ask: "What do you smell like?"

Anna didn't seem conscious of her scent at all. She was now wearing a lovely, floaty, Laura Ashley-style flowery dress. A mere waft of a hand could move the material. The dress clung to Anna's voluptuous female frame and accentuated her gentle movements and every curve on her incredible body.

Still, all that couldn't disguise the odour, which I now had no doubt was coming from her. It was sour, overpowering and very disturbing – sort of like rotting fish. Smell is one of our most powerful senses. It is the first sense to spark off a memory, and I have to say that I don't want to remember this one again. Ever. There is really no excuse for sloth in this area.

Even worse, my imagination had leapt out of the plane and was now in free fall. I had all sorts of thoughts running through my brain as to where exactly that putrid smell was coming from. And I didn't want to be proven right as to my speculations.

Anna leant back on the bed provocatively, licked her lips and asked me how I was feeling. She then beckoned me to come closer. But the spell between us had been broken by the smell between us. I was actually starting to feel nauseous. Unknown to her, I had already sent my cousin Steve a text asking him to call me urgently and to shout loudly down the phone, as though it was an emergency.

Steve was right on time. He called me before the saliva on Anna's lips had dried and screamed loudly enough down the phone for Anna to hear, leaving her in no doubt as to my need to leave her and go to his rescue. I quickly apologised to her for the emergency and told her I'd call her later. How many people on a date have pulled that excuse out in order to escape? I doubt whether many have done it while in someone's bedroom.

I managed to look upset that we had been interrupted and told Anna I had to run, quite literally, to save Steve. I then sprinted down the road, just in case she was watching from the window. I stopped as soon as I turned the corner, panting for breath.

Anna's odour was still in my nostrils, but thankfully I passed a McDonald's restaurant on the way back and the pleasant aroma of their fast food erased the smell within a few minutes.

Anna and I never spoke again after that odoriferous evening.

DEADLY SIN: WRATH

Sofia

I made contact with Sofia through Elite Singles.com. They had quite an in-depth matching profile process, which appeared fairly accurate and seemed to work well. Sofia and I were matched on our tastes in music and our love of exotic beach holidays. I love a beach with pure white sand and a warm sea. I like it when the waves are inviting yet tenacious.

Sofia was really something to look at. 5ft5, with a slim body, high cheekbones, wavy, light-brown hair and the best part, the most incredible blood red lips. She was Russian, not just Russian, not just beautiful, but she had a degree in Marketing and Business Studies. She was 36.

So I thought, "Well, why not?"

I sent her the first message and we chatted online for a few days before speaking on the phone two or three times. Her voice was as amazing as those lips. Thankfully, she met most of the important points on my checklist too.

Sofia was still learning to speak English, but her English was better than my Russian and her accent was lovely to listen to. Her pictures, profile and our flirting made me think that there was a spark between us that I would like to light up.

It wasn't until we decided to meet up that things started to get interesting. Sofia told me she was based in London but was working in Istanbul for two months. If I wanted to meet up with her I'd have to wait for a few weeks until she came back. I felt impatient, so I asked if she could come back for a weekend.

Sofia said she couldn't. She worked in Turkey as a hotel concierge on a seasonal, fixed contract. She had to capitalise on the opportunity and grab the work while she had the chance. I respected that. I liked that she worked hard and was still amusing to talk to. She was quite balanced and I found this attractive. I think it's more important for a person to be balanced than to have any particular outstanding qualities.

Then Sofia flipped the script and asked me if I would come to visit her.

The fact that she was Russian, lived in London and worked in Istanbul made me appreciate her in a different way. She was transatlantic and I would have to pursue her if I wanted to meet her. So I pursued her. I booked a two-day trip to Istanbul so that we could have our FD.

Maybe the costs involved were more than they would be for a local date, but I had the time off and the travel costs for two days weren't expensive, as it was out of season. And I would get the chance to visit a new city and meet a gorgeous woman.

I believe you reap what you sow in life. If you want a chance at love then you need to invest in it. Many people don't even want to be full members of dating sites.

They simply register for free and browse profiles out of a tentative action to date. I think this is such a waste of time because if you're not going to do it properly, then why bother at all?

I flew into Istanbul, checked into my hotel and went to visit the picturesque Blue Mosque while I waited for Sofia. She was going to finish her shift by 7pm so that we could meet afterwards. I can't lie, I felt like James Bond. I was flying around the world meeting Russian chicks for love.

At around 6:30, Sofia called to tell me that annoyingly she was expected to work late on a double shift and that she wouldn't finish until around 11pm. Of course, I was disappointed. I had been eagerly anticipating our date.

"Baby," she purred in her sexy Russian accent. "I'm so sorry."

I tried to sound like I was OK with it and casually asked her where she was working so that I could go and see her. She went quiet for a few seconds and then she said in that gorgeous accent: "Baby, I have something to tell you. I am working in a nightclub, not a hotel. I am only a waitress here. I hope you are not mad at me, baby?"

"Oh no," I said quickly, trying to reassure her. I didn't want her to think I was a snob. I've had many jobs myself in my life and I don't think what you do for a living necessarily defines you. Besides which, the way she kept calling me "baby" in that Russian accent was slowly defusing any possibility of me being annoyed with her.

"I'll come down to see you anyway," I said smoothly. "I can have a drink and enjoy the music until you're finished."

"OK, baby," she said demurely. "When you come inside come to bar, ask for me and I come to see you."

This was no longer going according to plan. For a moment I checked myself. Sofia had lied about her job. I wondered what else she might be lying about. I realised that I was in a foreign country just for a date. I wondered whether I had overlooked common sense and made a silly move in my eagerness to meet Sofia.

"Don't be silly, JP," I told myself. "It's just a date and you've nothing to lose."

I got dressed in some grey jeans and a black shirt. I looked pretty good for a first date. I took the tube to the area where Sofia worked. It was a busy street and it wasn't hard to find the nightclub. From the outside it looked swanky and expensive. The club's name glowed in blue and green neon lights on the outside wall and the windows were tinted dark blue.

An evil looking bouncer on the door let me in, only after giving me dagger looks. He had several craters in his face, which looked like souvenirs from a fight club membership. He seemed to be searching for something with that intense glare, but I couldn't quite work out what it was. There was a tingling in the back of my neck and I tensed up for a moment before I went in.

Later, when I thought back, I realised what an absolute dickhead I'd been by going to a foreign country for the first time for a FD in an unknown nightclub. James Bond was probably better prepared than me to handle these kinds of situations.

As I went down into the basement, I heard music and immediately felt more relaxed. Pharrell and Jay-Z greeted me with the song *Frontin'*. The baseline was reverberating along my spine like it was playing a Xylophone on my C1 and C2 vertebrae. I'm a big muso and the song made me feel at home.

Once my eyes had adjusted to the low lights, I could see several tables around the dance floor, where four poles had been positioned. For a minute my mind flickered back to Madeline and I smiled to myself. She would probably have a good time here! The club was quite small but intimate, with maybe 50 patrons.

I passed a table, where a beautiful girl was sitting by herself. She smiled at me after catching my eye.

"Maybe she's a dancer," I thought to myself. The vibes in the club were mellow and chilled. I couldn't believe I'd been nervous about coming to meet Sofia at the club. Obviously I was out of practice at being adventurous.

"This is great," I thought. "I've found a decent club to spend a quality evening in."

"Baby!" I heard whispered in my ear. I turned to see my lovely date Sofia. She wore flawless makeup and her hair had a wet look that made her appear sophisticated as well as sexy. She was dressed in a clingy tight black dress, which stopped half way down her thighs. Her legs were so well toned she could have been a Russian gymnast.

I took a sharp intake of breath. It was a moment to remember. For a waitress, Sofia looked very hot. I could understand why the nightclub would want to employ her. I would probably buy lots more drinks if a girl like her served me.

We gave each other a quick hug. Her body felt perfectly

toned. I listened as she told me she would need to work for a few hours before her shift ended. She asked if she could seat me and if I wanted a drink while I was waiting.

"A drink sounds good," I said keenly. Actually I was thirsty for a beer.

"Baby, can you sit next to my sister?" Sofia asked. "She is here for the evening to hang out with me and she would like to meet you, too."

Sofia sat me down next to the dazzling girl I had seen when I first walked into the club. The night was getting better by the minute. Sofia's sister was just as pretty, but in a different way. She looked about three years younger, in her early to mid-30s.

"This is Anastasia," Sofia said, sitting me down next to her sister and then taking a seat on my other side.

Now, I did know that I wasn't there to date Anastasia, but the situation I'd found myself in gave my ego a considerable boost. I puffed out my chest proudly. I felt pretty good about being sat between these two gorgeous Russian sisters. I wasn't quite sure what to expect next, but for a first date it all felt pretty exciting.

The moment I sat in between these two fabulously glamorous Russian girls, a Turkish waiter appeared and nodded at me. It's funny how a man will respect another man when he has a beautiful woman by his side. It can really do a lot for a man's street cred, and here I was with two beauties. My street cred was off the Richter scale.

"Have a look at the menu, sir," the waiter said, handing one over. I scanned the drinks and did a quick mental calculation, converting Turkish Lira to pounds. It looked like the average alcoholic beverage was about £10. It certainly wasn't cheap, but I decided it was manageable for a round or two.

I ordered a beer for me and the two girls asked for a glass of wine each. I hadn't eaten anything since landing in Istanbul, as I had expected to meet up with Sofia earlier, and I was actually pretty hungry. Unfortunately, there was no food on the menu. The girls were in a bubbly mood and we chatted and joked as great music played in the background and the drinks started to warm us up.

To avoid getting drunk, I munched down all the complimentary peanuts. I forgot I was supposed to be dating Sofia. Instead I found myself having a relaxed and flirty time with both women.

A couple of times I danced with either Sofia or Anastasia on the dance floor. Several times I danced with both of them around the poles. Both of them were good dancers. They complimented me on my Justin Timberlake moves and we were rocking. Music, dancing and beautiful ladies. What more could a guy want?

Intermittently the waiter appeared at our table, as if he'd been teleported there. Our drinks were constantly refilled without us needing to ask. It got to the point where I couldn't tell whether I'd drunk from the same glass twice.

But I didn't worry. Prince was screaming *"Get Off!"* The music was so pelvis-thrusting funky that it made me want to gyrate.

Both the girls had fallen for me. It seemed I would soon have to pick. It would be a tough choice, as they were both so incredibly sexy. By now I was slightly tipsy, although not quite drunk. The night had brought me something completely different and unexpected. The last song came on and people started to leave the dance floor. Some were leaving the club.

I called the waiter for my bill, while the two sisters linked arms with mine. They were being affectionate and flirty. They began chirping away between themselves in Russian while I sat with them feeling bemused by the conversation and what it implied.

The waiter appeared again to give me the bill and I checked it before offering my card to pay. There were no handheld terminals, so I had to go to the bar. I calculated the bill to be roughly £200 for 20 drinks. We'd had about six each. It was an expensive bill for me, but at that moment all I could think about was that my date had multiplied.

The benefit, this time, seemed to have outweighed the cost...

I handed over my card and the manager smiled at me while swiping it.

"Sorry, it's declined," he said. "Do you have another card?"

"My friend, my card has a £1000 limit and I'm well within it," I replied firmly. "Try it again."

"I try four times," he said. "It doesn't work. Have you different card?"

"I don't understand," I said. "My limit is £1000 and the bill is roughly £200. It must be your system at fault here. Can you check it?"

"Sir," he said in a menacing tone. "Your bill is nearly £2,000. There's nothing wrong with system."

I was stunned. I checked the menu and calculated the price of a drink. It wasn't £10, as I had initially ascertained. It was £100. Per drink.

"How can these drinks be £100 each? For one drink? For a beer?" I asked. I was really confused.

"You have girls sit with you," the man replied. "Girls cost money. Girls not free. You pay now!"

In that moment I understood which girls he was referring to. Sofia and Anastasia. The girls I had been plying with drinks all night were the club's escorts.

The manager wasn't smiling any more and suddenly the evil-looking bouncer from the door appeared next to me. Everyone who worked at the club seemed to be able to teleport at will. But neither of the guys had a pleasant bedside manner and I knew they would be trouble if I didn't pay the bill.

I complained loudly about settling up, saying I hadn't known about the high prices. The problem was that it was all clearly written on the menu. The dynamic duo threatened to call the police if I didn't pay up. I remembered that the other guys in the club hadn't been ordering as many drinks as me. No wonder the waiter was so busy around our table.

I realised I was being legally robbed.

As I couldn't pay with the card via the till, both men accompanied me out of the club, up the street and to the nearest cashpoint. They looked like my bodyguards, as they were so close to me the whole time. I withdrew my daily limit of £1000 and paid them. I promised to return the next day with the rest.

After much arguing and some angry threats from the ugly duo, I managed to convince them that I had paid them the most I could before they decided to call it a night and let me go.

All in all, it had been a pretty scary experience. I didn't know exactly how much these guys knew about me from Sofia. Would she tell them which hotel I was in? I rang a friend to let him know what had happened and he advised me to leave the next day, or to at least change hotels.

I wondered exactly how girls like Sofia and Anastasia managed to sleep at night. They must have been drinking Horlicks before bed by the crate load. Sofia had managed to separate me from my money by introducing herself via a dating site. Then she had used her henchmen's wrath to extort money from me. I'd been so gullible.

As I walked back to my hotel, I made a mental note that this date had been the most expensive one so far. There had certainly been no opportunity to go Dutch in Turkey with these Russians. It had been silly and overly spontaneous of me to travel to a foreign country and meet up with someone after chatting to them online for a few days. I should have waited until my 'date' was at least in the same area as me, and I shouldn't have agreed to meet up in unfamiliar surroundings. Dating via the internet is already difficult enough to get right, without complicating the whole thing with spontaneous acts of international courtship.

You never know who you're meeting in real life and should exercise some care when meeting someone for the first time. That means staying in familiar surroundings, such as your own country. And this rule applies to both sexes.

James Bond might travel around the world in *From Russia with Love*, but I'd been strung up in Turkey.

DEADLY SIN: PRIDE

Naomi

I met Naomi through Lovestruck. I thought I'd give the site a try, as they had really nice looking members. Naomi had two children, one of whom was a teenager. She worked as a social worker and enjoyed her job because it involved helping children. That sounded good to me because I was looking for someone who could help me with mine!

Naomi had a large family and liked spending time with them. They enjoyed get-togethers, meeting for dinners in the week and going for days out by the sea at the weekend. That sounded appealing and healthy to me. She also liked to play basketball. She had short-ish brown hair and was 5ft8, with lovely curves and an athletic body. I do like strong women.

We spoke on the phone twice, each time for about an hour. The conversation was light but relaxed and I found Naomi easy to get on with. I subtly ran my checklist past her, in between our banter, and she came up trumps.

For our first date we arranged to meet at Bluewater Shopping Centre, as it was conveniently halfway between our respective homes. For a date, we met quite early, about 11am. This was because I didn't want to face too much traffic either side of our meet up.

When I arrived at Bluewater, Naomi was in the process of calling my mobile to check where I was. She was obviously impatient, having arrived just before me. This made me feel desired and in demand. I liked the attention.

"This is cool," I thought.

A few minutes later we met and exchanged kisses, one on each cheek, just like the French do.

In person, Naomi was much more impressive than in her pictures. Because of her job she had been careful with the photographs she had put up. She had taken them from a distance, making it seem as if you were looking at her through a pair of binoculars the wrong way round. In person she was rather sumptuous. Her shoulder length, dark brown hair complimented her brown eyes, light red lips and soft-looking smooth skin. She was edible.

Descriptions are always odd on dating sites. When people use the terms 'slim' or 'athletic' or even 'average' to describe their bodies, they don't always seem to appreciate what the common understanding of those descriptions is. I won't go into exactly what those terms mean, but if I had to assign some celebrity females to those descriptions I'd choose Gwyneth Paltrow, Venus Williams and Taylor Swift, in that order.

Naomi had described herself as athletic, and that's exactly what she was. She didn't turn up with a body that was far from that description. So she was honest and straightforward. Does someone's body description matter? Yes it does!

After meeting, we went for a walk around Bluewater.

Like many alpha males, I don't like shopping centres or even shopping, but Naomi made it a pleasant experience for me by focusing on shops that would interest men. I listened to her opinions on men's fashion and gadgets and actually found myself debating them with her and getting past the usual superficial chitchat of a FD.

The one item she got really excited about was the Tesla 3 car on display. She insisted on pulling me into the store to leer over it, from seats to engine. She pointed out that it would benefit the world by helping to save fossil fuel energy. And it had great reviews for its speed and comfort. We got very involved in the subject of electric cars, and this was surprisingly entertaining.

First dates are high-pressure meetings where there are high expectations to like each other quickly. This is not always realistic, as usually it takes longer than one date to get to know and like someone. Unless the date is a Deadly one, I think you could take a chance and go for another one to see if anything further develops between the two of you.

Naomi was nice. Nice and funny and attractive.

We sat down in a patisserie and had breakfast together. Scrambled eggs, smoked salmon and coffee. It was heaven. I could feel myself starting to warm to this woman in front of me.

"This feels great," I thought. "The search is over. I've found someone I can gel with. It's Will Smith and Jada Pinkett all over again."

We continued chatting and gently bonding. We talked about our lives, our kids and our homes, as well as our desires in a relationship. Men and women seem to hold different views on what's important to talk about on a first date.

Most of the women I've dated are interested in what I do for a living, how much it demands of my time and how much I roughly earn. They want to know if I could support them if they wanted me to. They're not gold diggers but they do want to know if I would be able to take care of them. Could I be chivalrous enough to be their King, even if it was with a Mastercard?

They are also interested in where I live. Location is very important. Do we live far from each other? They are also curious if I own my home or if I'm renting. Or if I'm sharing a room. Will they be comfortable if they visit me?

They usually ask about my relationship status. Am I divorced or separated? Do I have a lot of contact with the baby mother? How many dates have I been on? How long have I been single? Do I have children and how often do I see them? How much drama will they have to absorb?

You get the idea. A lot of first dates involve a subtle interrogation about my life based on the checklist that she has. She has a list of expectations that I pleasingly try to contort myself into, hoping that I will impress her enough for her to want to see me again. In the meantime, I try to check out the things that are important to me, namely body, face and temperament.

After the checklist has been dealt with, the next important thing is chemistry. If there isn't any then it doesn't matter about the rest of the list. There must be a sense of attraction between us.

Naomi was very innovative about finding out what kind of person I was. She was a bright girl and went on to ask me a list of low-key questions about certain choices I would make in certain situations. Then she analysed them for me and told me what kind of woman I was looking for.

"What colour do you associate with yourself?" she asked.

"Turquoise blue," I answered.

"That means you think of yourself as relaxed, open and spiritual," she said thoughtfully after a minute.

"What kind of animal would you like to be?"

"Maybe a lion," I said.

"That's because a lion is powerful, solid and strong, but graceful and protective of its young, as well as beautiful," she said.

She told me these were the qualities I probably wanted in a woman too. I wasn't sure I agreed with her view, but I was enjoying the courtship.

She asked me about five questions in total, and each time she wrote down my answers and told me about what they meant. This whole conversation took about half an hour, but it was pretty entertaining and she gave me a lot of attention by offering a listening ear and providing a friendly synopsis of my desires in a woman.

We left the coffee shop and went to a wine bar, where Naomi bought us Prosecco and some snacks. We continued the banter and talked playfully about a second date location, allowing ourselves to relax a little more with each other. Naomi was very good company. Why she was still single I had no idea.

It's quite hard for me to enjoy a date and also analyse it all at the same time. It's similar to enjoying your own wedding. You want so much for it to go well that to plan and execute it and enjoy the whole experience is hard. You probably enjoy it more when you later watch the video footage.

Maybe I should get TMZ (the entertainment news crew) to film my dates.

This date was unfolding pretty well. On top of that, the two of us had attracted the attention of some of the staff at the wine bar, who had figured out we were on a date. They asked us how we had met and wanted all the details about our date so far.

It's funny how curious people get when they observe couples on a date. I think the possibility of love really interests the public. They have been fed Hollywood films like *Pretty Woman* for breakfast, lunch and dinner for so long that they really think it can happen. Maybe it can, but through a dating site?

The bar staff helped our date along by being extra attentive to us. They gave us great service. It was like having our own personal entourage and they seemed keen for Naomi and me to get on really well. Maybe they just wanted a good tip.

It was towards the end of the glass of Prosecco that I realised what had been staring me in the face for the whole of our date without me ever thinking about it.

Naomi was attractive, but I wasn't attracted to her. It's not easy to describe why you're not attracted to someone physically, especially if they're conventionally good looking. It's just something you either feel or you don't. It's not too complicated and you don't have to justify it to your date in any way.

We were really comfortable with each other, but there seemed to be something a bit motherly about Naomi. She was acting like a big sister and seemed to be enjoying this role. This had somehow managed to cause the chemistry between us to glitch and there was just no attraction from my side. I've been out with girls before whom I don't fancy. Once I know how I feel, I switch into friendship mode.

On reflection, the whole shopping together episode and Naomi analysing my desires in a woman seemed more like the actions of an older sister than a potential lover. Maybe she thought that I wasn't a good match for her and she was just styling it out really well. I thought that as we had established a friendship and were enjoying the date, I would take the opportunity to speak with Naomi openly about the future.

Big Mistake.

"I really am glad we've met up and got to know each other. You're exactly as you described yourself. It makes a change to meet someone who is actually honest on the internet. You and me are going to have a good friendship, I can feel it," I said confidently as we both faced the bar.

"How do you mean?" she asked, turning to look at me.

"Well…" I continued digging the hole. "Everyone seems to post stuff about themselves that isn't true. But you're not like that. And even though we're not attracted to each other physically, we're having such a good time as friends that it would be great to keep in touch. It would be good to hang out again sometime."

Naomi's eyes narrowed and her eyebrows seemed to almost touch each other, as if they were joining forces to form an expression.

"Are you saying you don't find me attractive? That's a bit bloody rude, isn't it?" she said soberly.

I was looking for the humour in her face but if there was any, it was hiding behind a very tense looking mask. She looked like she was about to combust and fire off into orbit.

"No, no, I don't mean it like that. I mean we're not attracted to each other." I tried very hard to keep my voice even and factual. "I'm saying that I'd still like to keep in touch with you as a friend. It's good that there's no pressure to arrange to see each other again. But it's been a good date and such a good laugh."

Even as I said it I knew the laughs had now become extinct.

"I feel like you're more like a sister than a woman I fancy," I said, trying to explain.

Naomi opened her mouth as though she was about to respond with some choice words, but instead closed it again. Her face became emotionless.

"Your sister!" she finally blurted out. "What are you, some sort of pervert?"

I stopped trying to explain because I knew it was pointless. She was already in orbit.

She was silent for a moment. Then she said dryly, "Yeah, I feel the same actually. I didn't fancy you either. I couldn't feel a spark between us. I was just waiting for the right time to say it."

Naomi's whole attitude had changed. She went from being friendly and chatty to really sullen and moody. I couldn't believe the contrast in the two personalities that had been on display within the same minute. I had really put my foot in it by giving her open feedback about our date. Once again, honesty was not the best policy. I hoped that I hadn't offended her.

I thought she had finished her outburst, but she was just warming up.

"The problem with guys like you is that you're all the same," she said. "You either go out with me and want to get into my knickers straight away, or you're married with your wife at home and you're looking for a bit of fun, or you've got no job and want to sponge off of me."

I wanted to point out that I didn't fancy her enough to want to get into her knickers, that I wasn't married and had a job, but it didn't seem to be a good time. I wondered if I should offer her some money for the Prosecco she'd bought. Then again, that might set her off again.

She continued: "This dating stuff is just a load of crap! Men are just a load of blagging liars and it's bloody boring hearing the same stories every time." Then her voice took on a contemptuous tone. "I like guys who are taller than you and usually the chemistry is way better for me too. I was just about to tell you that I'm going home soon, as I don't want to waste any more time here."

She stood up proudly, her pink lips pouting. She seemed to be pretty annoyed, but she still had great posture. I must have offended her in my ignorance. So much for our new friendship! I think if I were going to ask the questions that she'd asked me earlier on, right then her colour would have been red.

By now the bar staff were smirking away behind her back, but when they walked in front of her they had the sombre faces of funeral-goers. I was a bit embarrassed at Naomi's public display of emotion. We Brits don't really do public emotions, apart from at football matches. I think the staff had firmly taken us out of the category of *Pretty Woman* romance and put us alongside *The Exorcist*.

I put my hand out to Naomi in an attempt to cool her down a bit so that she would take her seat again. I thought maybe we could salvage something positive from the date, but she was too wired now. She pulled back, looking at my hand like I had leprosy, and then picked up her jacket and handbag. I felt a bit relieved that she was leaving and I think the staff did, too.

"Well, it's been great to meet up and I'm sorry I've offended you. I hope we can keep in touch. Shall I walk you to your car?" I asked, hoping she would say no.

"Don't bother. I've already blocked you on WhatsApp, so don't try to message me!"

Naomi turned towards the door and walked off. She looked great, even from the rear. And that was it. My date had left the building. It seemed a real shame, as I had really enjoyed our time together and thought we could at least have been friends. But I'd clearly damaged her pride and there was no coming back from it.

Although the date hadn't ended well, I had to congratulate myself on my progress in dating decorum. My checklist had been ticked all the way through. No major surprises had been revealed during our date. We looked like our photos. We'd had some friendly fun. And our body odour was pleasant. Later, I asked myself whether I should have gone out with Naomi at least twice to see if any chemistry developed. Maybe my sense of attraction had been faulty.

But Naomi's reaction had revealed that she had a bit of a short fuse. I was glad I'd avoided Kid Dynamite.

DEADLY SIN: ENVY

Phoebe

I began chatting with pretty Phoebe on Christian Connection after she sent me an online wave. She looked like she was a model, although her photos could have been airbrushed. Her cheekbones were high and her lips naturally pouting and rosy. She had black hair, which flowed past her shoulders, and dark brown eyes. She was 38, 5ft6, described herself as athletic and looked in good physical shape.

We were a good match physically because of our athleticism and compatible height. We both liked spending time with our families and had a similar fondness for animals and children. Phoebe had two grey Siamese cats, which she doted on.

Phoebe and I didn't waste time. We spoke on the phone the same day we connected online, and we met the next day. That was efficient and made me feel that she was serious about wanting to date someone. So many online daters want to chat online for days to get to know someone, but it's not a good way of finding out more, because people are not what they type.

Don't believe the type!

The person you get to know via Snapchat, Instagram, Twitter, Facebook or even WhatsApp is not the person they are in private. It's their public representative.

When we spoke on the phone, Phoebe sounded very calm and laid back. She also had a dry sense of humour. She worked as a Manager for a vehicle distribution company and spent quite a bit of time travelling around and staying in different parts of the country.

Phoebe had a decent job, was gorgeous and had a pleasant phone voice. She had no kids and had been single for about a year. My pre-date checklist had ticks all the way through it.

She was ready to meet me and I was keen to see if I would be able to explore new territory with my national traveller.

We met at All Bar One in Beckenham. I arrived first and waited to be seated. I got a table but it was incredibly dirty. So, knowing that Phoebe would be arriving at any moment, I got a tissue and tried to clean it myself. Of course, bang in the middle of me wiping, I looked up to see Phoebe standing in front of me with a huge smile on her face.

I was a bit embarrassed to look like a cleaner on our first date, but Phoebe seemed impressed that I was making an effort for her. I stopped cleaning and took a good look at her. She was wearing figure hugging blue jeans and a red blouse.

I like women who are active and try to stay in shape. It's important to me. This works both ways. Almost every woman I've met appreciates a man who tries to keep in reasonable condition and isn't a slob.

Women do check out men's bodies, but they're not usually as obvious about it. In these times I think a man has a greater need to stay in physical shape. Women quite often exercise and release their frustrations in the gym. So a guy should stay in shape, too, and give a woman confidence that he can physically take care of her.

Most men like to relax after a day's work. We like to watch TV or hit the PlayStation, if we haven't stopped off to see our mates for a drink first. It can be frustrating for some women if they have to work the same hours in a job, as well as take care of the home and then stay in shape on top of all that. It's as if she's having to man up while us guys are enjoying our metrosexuality.

Phoebe and I kissed each other on the cheek and sat down to chat. We seemed to have lots to talk about and bantered for a long time, getting to know the important things about each other: our family backgrounds, our jobs, our religious beliefs, our previous relationships and our future plans. We seemed very compatible.

Phoebe wasn't really a drinker, but we enjoyed a glass of wine together and there was an air of attraction moving nicely around us. We had each other's full attention and the rest of the bar just seemed to fade away for a while. What I really appreciated about my date was her superb manners. It was obvious that this was a very classy woman.

The whole time we were chatting, we were also checking each other out. Phoebe looked really hot. She said she went running regularly and she sure looked fit. She told me she thought I was better looking in person than in my pictures. I liked that. I duly complimented her on her own loveliness.

Women can be insecure about their looks and bodies, yet they still desire attention. All the while we men can't stop looking at them and thinking about their bodies. It's a perfect match designed to keep our species feeding each other's needs.

The music was getting loud in the bar and it was getting hard to hear each other. Phoebe had a lovely voice. It had almost a musical lilt, even though she said she couldn't sing. She spoke very calmly and patiently, which made me think that we would be able to communicate well together. It seemed like finally I'd found a good match. Could this be The One?

Direct and straightforward, Phoebe said she liked me and didn't often go on dates because she was quite fussy. She described herself as having high standards and expectations. My ears pricked up at this titbit of information.

I used to think that if a woman has high standards and she's with me, then logically this must mean I'm an exceptional man and must have better qualities than my competition. Sadly, I've learned that this isn't the case. If she says that she has high standards, she is not telling me I've *met* them. She is telling me she believes I *will* be capable of meeting them in the future.

My ego heard Phoebe's words before my ears, so I didn't really think about her statement. Instead, I focused on the developing attraction between us. I saw nine stone of shapely flesh, a gorgeous face and a great personality on display. We men are, after all, simple creatures. Our lists of requirements are pretty simple: love, food and sleep. I've found that many women's 'keep-me-happy' lists are a bit longer and subject to change.

Phoebe and I were both feeling hungry, so we left and went to a Thai restaurant a few doors away. We both liked Thai food and the taste of the east seemed a good way to continue our courtship. But when we sat down to order, Phoebe didn't seem too ravenous and only ordered two starters and a coke.

This seemed strange to me, considering how starving she'd said she was. I enjoy having a drink with friends and drinking alone is never as much fun. Even so, I ordered myself a glass of Chenin Blanc. I've been out with women who are t-total before. It's strange drinking while those around you are stone cold sober. You don't need to get drunk to have fun, but I think it's nice to enjoy a drink and relax with the effect it brings.

We were in the middle of our food when Phoebe decided to tell me more about her life.

It's important to get to know someone before expecting them to divulge more personal information, and quite right, too. I wouldn't post intimate details of my life on the internet for everyone to see. However, I think that when you talk to a potential date on the phone, you could bring up some things that are important and might even stop someone from wanting to meet you.

While I was having my Pad Thai noodles and Tom Yum soup, Phoebe told me she wanted a baby.

It was like a scene from *Only Fools and Horses*. My soup got stuck in my throat and my noodles fell all over the table.

"Sorry?" I spluttered. "I don't understand."

Phoebe explained that she had been having tests at a fertility clinic and was due to begin treatment any time soon. She had decided to have a baby by herself, as, at 38, she felt her biological clock was ticking and she hadn't met anyone with whom she wanted to start a family.

That was until now, of course.

"You're such a wonderful man," she told me. "I've been waiting for a while now for a good man and someone to have a child with. I think you would make such a good father and I can't believe that I've been lucky enough to have met you."

I thought that it might be a passing thought or a really bad attempt at making a joke. I smiled weakly to avoid responding to Phoebe's statement, but she didn't stop there.

"I know it's only our first date, but I want to be upfront and honest about my intentions."

Phoebe had a plan and hoped to be a mother in the next year. She wanted any potential future man in her life to know this immediately. Well, immediately after meeting each other, at least. I had to respect that much. At least she didn't lie to me or try to hide this nugget of information.

"Phoebe, I really have enjoyed our date, and even though one day in the future I'd like to have more children and maybe even get married, I don't think I can plan to have a child with a woman I've just met," I said. I was starting to get that familiar sinking feeling.

"Of course not," Phoebe said, as though I was being stupid.

Maybe I'd got all this wrong? I was hopeful we still had a chance. She was so lovely and we had been getting on really well. Surely we could get past this conversation and head in a more romantic direction?

She continued. "Not right now today, obviously. But I really want so badly to be a mum and I keep looking at all those other mums with their kids. I'm so envious of them. Surely you can understand that? Please just give it some thought.

"I'm going to need a sperm donor," she explained, "because apparently my eggs are in short supply and I have to move on with this as soon as possible. What I'd like is if *you* could be the donor because that way if we *do* get together in the future, at least the man I'm with is the father, rather than some random stranger. Please just think about it."

I was actually thinking about it quite intensely. I was wondering what planet Phoebe came from and if I'd somehow managed to take a quantum leap into another person's life.

I also despaired again about meeting up with someone who I was hopeful about, only to find they hadn't been upfront about their intentions. I realised that it's only by meeting someone can you understand them, unless you discuss these kinds of issues before you meet.

I could see that my checklist was going to have to be revamped. Maybe I'd have to approach a first date like a speed date. I read somewhere once about a man who spent only one hour on a first date, just to gather all the essentials. Just like a proper interview structure. This is the advantage of speed dating, as it involves meeting face-to-face and going through a checklist of questions inside a set number of minutes. Imagine a five-minute date.

As we finished our food and drinks, I noticed that Phoebe had now lost her relaxed manner. Instead she kept looking at me as though she wanted me to say something about her request. I felt an unspoken pressure to answer 'yes' or 'no' as soon as possible.

"I don't live far from here," Phoebe said. "Would you like to come back to my place for a drink?" She smiled encouragingly now and reached for my hand.

I think that if a woman suggests coming back to her place on a first date, it doesn't mean she's loose or has dishonourable intentions. Even if that's what you're hoping, it probably isn't the case. She probably likes you and trusts you, which shows you must have made a good impression. In any other situation, just like I'd done with Anna, I would have gone with Phoebe and enjoyed the rest of the evening.

The problem was that everything had got very serious all of a sudden. If I went back and she wanted to get more comfortable physically, I knew I wouldn't be certain whether Phoebe wanted me or whether she was just after my sperm. It wasn't sexy at all.

Men don't often need to think about the consequences of having sex *before* having it. Here I was being forced to think about the consequences of my actions *before* actually going to Phoebe's house. She was hungry to get pregnant and I was the honoured one, chosen to offer my sperm as a sacrifice to the cause.

I really didn't feel like having any physical involvement with Phoebe. What we had discussed had acted like bromide. It was an anti-aphrodisiac. I began to feel disconnected from her and suddenly wanted to just leave and go home.

I yawned very widely and checked the time on my Samsung. "I'd love to come, but I've got to go home, Phoebe," I said. "I have a really early start tomorrow".

I think she could see that she'd dropped a bomb and she nodded without speaking. I avoided saying anything else because she looked really emotional and I ran the risk of copping an explosion of tears.

I walked Phoebe back to the station and we kissed goodbye.

"Let me know what you think as soon as possible," she said, searching my face for any clues regarding my decision.

"Of course I will," I said, trying to sound serious. "Goodbye."

I never contacted Phoebe again. The whole conversation had been way too intense and forward for me. How could someone go on a dating website while they are actively trying to have a baby and not think to mention it before meeting a guy? I really needed to expand my range of questioning for future phone conversations. At the rate that my checklist was evolving, the questioning before each date would take days to complete and would probably sound like an insurance quote checklist from *Compare the Market*.

As I walked to the tube, I thought about Phoebe and how stunning she was. She really did have it all: looks, body and brains. I wondered whether I'd have fallen for her lovely charms had she not been so open with me about her intentions and her all-consuming envy of women blessed with children.

In nine months' time, I could have been a dad.

AFTERWORD

My purpose when I started internet dating was to find a partner with whom I'm compatible. I knew it wouldn't be a simple job. I was divorced after a long-term marriage, over 40 and had two children who were a priority in my life. I wanted to develop a quality relationship with a woman who was attractive, kind, good company and emotionally intelligent. If I settled for less then that's exactly what I'd get.

I could take my time and choose what I desired in a woman because I really enjoy my own and my family's company. I wasn't in any rush to be deeply involved with someone who wasn't a good match. As an only child, I like my 'me time'. There are also many other advantages of being an only child, but they're for a different discussion.

At this point, you're probably thinking that these 7 Deadly Dates have discouraged me from dating. That would be far from the truth. Even though these dates were each Deadly in their own right, I learned something from each of them, which helped me to refine my checklist and the way in which I approached dating on the net.

It was fun dating, but being serious about finding a partner meant it was a bit frustrating meeting different women who turned out to be incompatible. I'm sure they felt the same about going out with me, too. Even if one in five people are meeting their partners on the net, that's still only a 20% chance. It's not a high probability, so it's best just to be patient.

The checklist approach will definitely help you. My initial one was based firstly on physical features such as the lady's height, body type, hair, complexion and looks. Then I moved onto her demographic fit. Her age, her relationship status, whether she had children, and the kind of job she had. But as I worked my way through my 7 Deadly Dates, I developed my checklist in greater detail.

Neither Stacey nor Madeline were honest about their looks, as their pictures were way out of date. Your date should send you a recent picture so you can see what they look like now, rather than when they had their profile pictures taken. You can verify their face and also ascertain if they have gained huge amounts of weight. Does that mean you're fickle? No it doesn't. You're entitled to your preference and don't forget that you're dating in reverse.

You don't want to be wasting lots of time meeting people who don't look like their pictures. Asking them about it outright is always a good option. People approach internet dating like they're selling their car online, so they don't mind airbrushing their profiles for you to see them at their best. Just ask them on the phone before meeting them whether their profile is true and accurate. Tell them that's the person you want to meet.

You should probably then extend your questions to ask them as much as possible about what's going on in their lives right now. Are they looking to move to another country? Are they in fairly good health? Do they have their own teeth? Is there anything else for you to know that might save you time upfront? We men need to ask more questions.

Stacey was cheeky and dishonest to disguise herself in her profile, and she was naive to think it wouldn't matter, but this doesn't mean she was a bad woman.

With Madeline, if we had got on well in areas other than

physical chemistry, then we might still have enjoyed a second date. Physical compatibility is much more common than mental or emotional compatibility. Whatever you experience, use that knowledge while you're dating to help refine your approach.

Zoe was a decent girl but she was incredibly intense. Still, she thought it was appropriate to go from no chemistry to trying to get some mouth-on-mouth action. I didn't feel comfortable being with her, or the lip service she demanded at the end of our date.

Anna was a dazzling specimen of a woman. She seemed almost perfect and very compatible, yet her personal hygiene was seriously in need of attention. Quite often my guy friends have told me I'm too picky. I meet all these beautiful women who are in amazing shape physically and yet I find things wrong with them. The implication is that I'm the Deadly one!

Sofia was alluring enough for me to stupidly travel to Istanbul, where her angry bodyguards almost cost me my limbs, but what if I hadn't gone there? Would I have ever really known what she did for a living? Probably not!

Naomi would have made a great friend, but apparently even friends don't see honesty as the best policy. I have learned from that experience to be more cautious in my revelations.

In Phoebe's case, I couldn't have known she needed my bodily fluids for her master plan to populate the planet, but I used that experience later on to ask girls if they still wanted to have children. That was the only issue I had with Phoebe, but it was a big one. She was so advanced in her life plan that there wasn't any room for a man who had plans of his own, too.

In all of these Deadly Dates, I am the common denominator. I have to ask myself if perhaps these dates went wrong due to something I did. Or maybe I'm just not a good match for these women. Yet I didn't lie, I didn't behave inappropriately and I was always hopeful that it might work out. I tried to be a decent gentleman even when presented with really disappointing situations. I think I conducted myself pretty well.

I have to be true to myself. Maybe my standards are high, but they are my standards that exude from my values and beliefs. I don't need to compromise on them because I'm happy to have a good relationship with myself in the meantime. Maybe I'll never meet someone who lives up to those standards, but that's not the point. The point is that I need to be true to them.

Most of the women I dated had checklists. I think it makes good sense to put one together after you've spent a bit of time thinking about what's important to you. Then try to subtly run your checklist past the person you're talking to. We guys are often a bit simple in our approach to dating because we go for what tickles our visual fancy. Then once we succeed in getting our lovely lady, we work out what she's about and how to deal with it. We have what I call a Pay As You Go approach! That might work unless, like me, you have kids and are looking for a serious relationship. Then you might have to be a bit more careful when looking.

It was fun to meet new people whilst dating, but not asking enough questions and not having enough in common meant I was wasting my time and energy.

Once you're on your date, it's worth having a Plan B to get you out of there if it's not working out for you. Phone a friend is always a good strategy. I had Steve on speed dial when I was with Anna, and that worked a treat.

Where you meet someone is also important. Going to visit Sofia in Istanbul was a dumb move. I wouldn't recommend international dates at all, unless, of course, you are James Bond. What that experience also taught me was that sometimes a bit of patience might stop you from being robbed. Even though I don't really like online chatting too much, I could have waited for Sofia to come back to the UK and then met up with her. Still, she was rather stunning!

I haven't lost hope in finding 'The One'. I think there are many women who could be a good fit, and it's just a question of time before I resume my search. I haven't found my partner yet because I took a lengthy break from dating in order to assess what I learned from each date. Then I thought how great it would be to share my 7 Deadly Dates with you.

Technology is great. It's helping us to meet a wide range of people more quickly. But people are always going to be different from their virtual profile. Sometimes they'll look completely different from their pictures. And I still think that sites need to find a category to describe body scent!

It's worth mentioning that it's not only women who commit these Deadly sins. Many guys do too. I've had the misfortune of hearing all about how men lie regarding all sorts of details, sometimes exaggerating their height by at least a foot. Do they think the woman won't notice?

I'm sure everyone has a horror story to tell from meeting people from the internet. But don't lose hope in finding your Happy Ever After. Get smarter and use technology as your tool to search for what you desire. Dating sites are still a good way to find what you want. I personally know couples that have met through the net and are now in happy relationships.

Well, you've read about my 7 Deadly Dates and shared my personal experiences. Maybe you have encountered some deadly dates of your own, and maybe you won't completely avoid them in the future. Still, turn up with reasonable expectations, keep an open mind and aim to have fun.

If you do have a funny experience, write it down and maybe one day you could share it with me.

Jean-Paul

About the Author

Jean-Paul Noel-Cephise is a former accountant, whose current job as a freelance lecturer takes him all over the world. He has also worked as a legal executive in Africa, the Middle East and Asia. Although he has written articles for various publications over the years, this is his first published book.

The father of two boys, Jean-Paul has studied and researched relationship psychology for many years. He has been a model and an actor and, during a sabbatical, he worked as a deep tissue massage therapist for a charity based in central London.

He enjoys writing in cafés, parks and anywhere that takes him out of his home environment. He loves to play sports or games of any kind and dancing is at the top of his list.

You can visit his website at www.7deadlydates.com or email him at spartan.jpnc@gmail.com

Acknowledgements

I'd like to thank the following people:

My children for inspiring my journey

My parents for providing me with a privileged childhood

My friends Joan Andrews, Michael Ringer, Joseph Martin
and Carl Townsend. Thanks for your help

My family Ginette and Siven. Also Chris and Ian,
for providing inspiration

My great teachers Mr Hathaway, Mike Barker and
Brandon Raynor

My mentors Petrina Haywood and Al Tenquist

My hard-working editor Danielle Wrate

My cousin Linda, who is always there for me

My dear uncles France and Pierre (R.I.P)